Abba's Heart

STUDY GUIDE

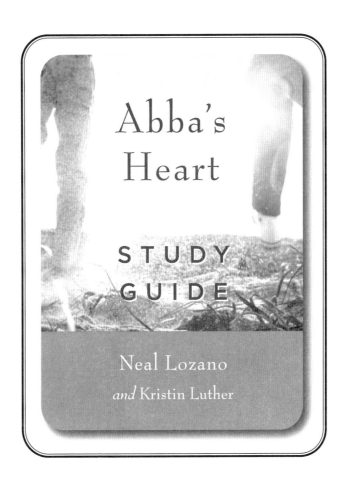

Abba's Heart

STUDY GUIDE

Neal Lozano

and Kristin Luther

Jubilee Studio

CLINTON CORNERS, NEW YORK

ABBA'S HEART: Study Guide
Neal Lozano and Kristin Luther

All Scripture quotations, unless otherwise indicated, are taken from the HOLY BIBLE, NEW INTERNATIONAL VERSION®. NIV®. Copyright © 1973, 1978, by Biblica, Inc.™ Used by permission of Zondervan. All rights reserved worldwide. www.zondervan.com. The "NIV" and "New International Version" are trademarks registered in the United States Patent and Trademark Office by Biblica, Inc.™

Original cover of *Abba's Heart: Finding our Way to the Father's Delight* designed by Dual Identity and used here courtesy of the publisher, Chosen Books, Bloomington, Minnesota, a division of Baker Publishing Group, Grand Rapids, Michigan.

Cover and text of *Abba's Heart: Study Guide* designed by Jubilee Studio.

JUBILEE STUDIO is an imprint of The Attic Studio Publishing House
P.O. Box 75 • Clinton Corners, NY 12514 • Phone: 845-266-8100
E-mail: AtticStudioPress@aol.com

PRINTED IN THE UNITED STATES OF AMERICA   5 4 3 2 1

ISBN-13: 978-1-946787-06-4
ISBN-10: 1-946787-06-X

Contact information:

HEART OF THE FATHER MINISTRIES
P.O. Box 905 • Ardmore, PA 19003 • 610-952-3019
Website: www.heartofthefather.com

• CONTENTS •

Section 1: The Way Home

Section 2: The Father's Heart

Section 3: Coming Home

continued on next page

Section 4: Life in the Father's House

CHAPTER 1
The Promise

1. What do you picture when you think of God as "father"?

   To express your ideas below, use words...

   _____

   _____

   _____

   _____

   ...and/or sketch your ideas:

2. What are some questions you have of Him?

   _____

   _____

   _____

   _____

3. How did you first encounter/meet God?

_____

_____

_____

_____

4. *Read John 20:11-18.*

   What is your response to this personal promise — *that you belong, that God is your Father?*

_____

_____

_____

_____

5. "In finding a father, we find something of _____." *p. 28.*

6. What are your expectations of a father?

_____

_____

_____

_____

7. In what ways do you or have you felt "fatherless"?

_____

_____

_____

_____

8. What prompts your desire to know Father God more?

_____

_____

_____

_____

_____

9. In what ways can you relate to any of the people mentioned in this chapter:

- *Mary: distressed at Jesus' absences and then unable to recognize Him*

- *Bilquis: startled/surprised by the notion of God as Father*

- *Rick: rejected by, resentful & angry towards his father*

- *Lucie: in need of fatherly touch and blessing*

_____

_____

_____

_____

_____

10. *Read John 1:18 and John 10:30.*

As you reflect on your past, in what ways can you say you have seen or experienced the Father drawing you to Himself?

_____

_____

_____

_____

CHAPTER 2

A
Broken Heart

1. Can you think of a story that has meant more to you, the more times you have read or heard it?

_____

_____

_____

_____

2. *Read Luke 15:11-32.*

   a. Do you tend to relate more to one of these sons?

_____

_____

_____

_____

b. Knowing the father in the parable represents your Father God, what comforts you most about the way this father relates to **both** of his sons?

_____

_____

_____

_____

c. List the traits we see displayed in the father's character towards his sons.

_____

_____

_____

_____

3. "Two foundational elements in Jesus' description of the Father are

   that He is _____ and _____" *p. 34.*

4. In what ways can you relate to God's pain and brokenheartedness over His children?

_____

_____

_____

_____

5. Think for a moment on the fact that *God chose you.* He willed you into existence and He holds you with love, despite the pain. How does this change your perspective?

_____

_____

_____

_____

_____

6. The Father's love for you is so personal — you're the lost sheep, the penny, the son in the parable. What is your heart's response to this truth?

_____

_____

_____

_____

_____

CHAPTER 3

The Tragedy of Slavery

1. In what way(s) did you experience separation or isolation from your parents as a child?

      — perhaps, like Joseph, a physical separation?

      — or, like Matt, an emotional separation?

_____

_____

_____

_____

_____

2. How has such loneliness or pain challenged your sense of identity?

_____

_____

_____

3. Write a story of homecoming that you love. It could be one you've heard or experienced, a story from a movie or book, or a story that you create now yourself.

_____

_____

_____

_____

_____

_____

4. List the five aspects of the nature of our slavery to sin. *pp. 44-45.*

1. _____

2. _____

3. _____

4. _____

5. _____

5. In what ways does God's goodness and love for you seem "veiled" or hidden?

_____

_____

_____

6. Are you able to recognize your bondage? What idols, crutches, and strategies to save yourself do you need to abandon?

_____

_____

_____

_____

_____

7. Which tends to hinder you most from calling on the Savior: pride, fear or unbelief? How?

_____

_____

_____

_____

CHAPTER 4

Adoption: From Slaves to Sons

1. Describe "the turning point of your life's story," when you received Jesus and became an adopted heir.

_____

_____

_____

_____

_____

2. "The Father chose to offer up His son for you so that you might become His _____ and _____ with Jesus." *p. 53*

3. How, like Ben-Hur, do we learn to become sons of God?

    _____

    _____

    _____

    _____

4. *Read Genesis 45:28 & 46:1-7 & 46:28-30 — and picture the scene of this reunion.*

    a. Describe how you imagine Jacob feeling.

    _____

    _____

    _____

    _____

    b. Describe Joseph's likely response.

    _____

    _____

    _____

    _____

5. Imagine God's joy, described at the top of page 56. What do you picture?

    _____

    _____

    _____

    _____

6 a. Of the questions included on the second half of page 56, which do you most sense a need to respond to?

_____

_____

_____

_____

   b. Choose one or two of the page 56 questions and write a prayer of response to God, allowing Him to take what enslaves you.

_____

_____

_____

_____

_____

_____

_____

_____

_____

_____

_____

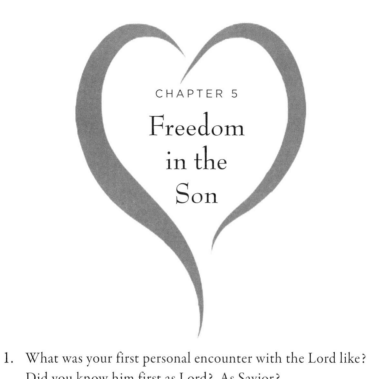

CHAPTER 5

Freedom in the Son

1. What was your first personal encounter with the Lord like?
   Did you know him first as Lord? As Savior?

   _____

   _____

   _____

   _____

2. In what ways has your brokenness drawn you nearer to the Lord?

   _____

   _____

   _____

   _____

3. "The Father is the One who sent the _____ who enables us to see and the _____ who reveals." *p. 61*

4. What things did your father do or not do, that you need to forgive him for? *(As you reflect on this question, you may want to seek the help of a trusted friend, pastor/priest, or spiritual mentor to help walk alongside you as you forgive and heal.)*

_____

_____

_____

_____

_____

_____

_____

5. What new freedoms does this forgiveness bring you into?

_____

_____

_____

_____

_____

_____

6. "True _____ means having your mind transformed by the truth about _____ you are and _____ you are, so you can choose the good in light of this reality." *p. 65*

7. As you read through the questions and prayer on page 67, what areas of your life are you aware of needing to repent of or release, in order to experience more freedom and to find your identity in the Father?

_____

_____

_____

_____

_____

CHAPTER 6

The Father's Heart

1. In what ways did you experience feelings like an orphan (lost, lonely, isolated, rejected, or abandoned) as a child?

_____

_____

_____

_____

2. "Knowing the Father reveals _____ as well as your own _____ in Him. Knowing the Father and your place in His _____ changes the landscape of your life." *p. 72*

3. As you read the section, "God Revealed Over Time," note two characteristics of God that stand out to you and help you know God more fully.

    _____

    _____

    _____

    _____

4. What is the "ultimate and complete self-revelation of God"? *p. 76*

    _____

    _____

    _____

    _____

5. What characteristics of the Father do we see in the actions and words of Jesus?

    _____

    _____

    _____

    _____

6. a. What do we learn of Father God through Jesus' prayers?

    _____

    _____

    _____

    _____

b. How do these insights, revealed through Jesus' actions, words and prayers, impact you and draw you to your Father?

_____

_____

_____

_____

7. Reflect on the image of this truth: *"The Father is eternally running to you."*

_____

_____

_____

_____

8. Consider the prompts and questions in this section, *"The Father Has Already Come to You."* Make note of the instances and ways, as you look back over your life, that you can see the Father making Himself known to you.

_____

_____

_____

_____

_____

_____

_____

_____

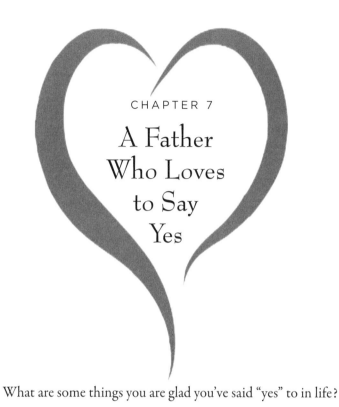

CHAPTER 7

A Father Who Loves to Say Yes

1. What are some things you are glad you've said "yes" to in life?

    _____

    _____

    _____

    _____

2. Have you ever withheld your heart from God, felt disappointed by or resentful towards Him? Explain.

    _____

    _____

    _____

    _____

3. a. What are our deepest needs? *p. 87*

_____

_____

_____

_____

    b. How can we have those needs met?

_____

_____

_____

_____

4. List some practical ways you can (a) pursue more of the Father's heart for you and (b) advance His Kingdom.

_____

_____

_____

_____

_____

_____

5. How do you respond to the idea that you are God's favorite?

_____

_____

_____

_____

6. What do you need to surrender, in order to really ask for God's will to be done?

_____

_____

_____

_____

7. How have the truths of this chapter impacted your prayer life and the way that you approach Him?

_____

_____

_____

_____

CHAPTER 8

Dreaming
of Home

1. What does home mean to you?

   _____

   _____

   _____

   _____

2. When you read "The Ideal Home," what is your response? In what
   ways does this description affirm or enhance your definition of
   home?

   _____

   _____

   _____

   _____

   _____

   _____

3. Who in your life has been like that mailman (on page 105), speaking a seed God planted? Share a memory of belonging, love, or childhood joy?

_____

_____

_____

_____

_____

4. What substitute(s) have you sought, throughout life, looking for intimacy, satisfaction, thrills, excitement, fortune, or fame?

_____

_____

_____

_____

_____

5. Describe any "came to my senses" moments that you have had in life.

_____

_____

_____

_____

_____

6. What has led you to seek "new direction" and follow God, at any point in your life?

_____

_____

_____

_____

_____

CHAPTER 9

Coming Home

1. What parts of your identity, your "old man," did you fear giving up, before the love of God transformed you?

_____

_____

_____

_____

2. a. Do you tend to respond to your sense of unworthiness with "denial encased in pride" or by giving "in to worthlessness and despair"?

_____

_____

_____

_____

b. How can you have more of a "humble receptivity to love"?

_____

_____

_____

_____

3. What is/has been "the truth about [your] life lived **without** God"? (In other words, what consequences of sin have you experienced, what are the things you've withheld) *pp. 115-116.*

_____

_____

_____

_____

_____

4. "[Repentance] is a _____ that begins with the realization of the _____ of God. . . . Repentance is a change of _____ that leads to a changed _____ as we see the reality of our sin in the light of God's love." *p. 116*

5. In what ways have you experienced "a new and glorious 'normal'" as a son/daughter of God? In what ways do you still desire more?

_____

_____

_____

_____

_____

_____

6. Take some time to confess your brokenness, your fears, your weakness before the Lord. Say *Yes* to the gift of the Father!

_____

_____

_____

_____

7. As you seek to identify with the Son, rather than sin, list some ways you want to "say yes to the Spirit."

_____

_____

_____

_____

CHAPTER 10

A New Foundation

1. What has your experience of "immediate" transformation by God
    been in your life?

    _____

    _____

    _____

    _____

2. How does Kerry's story speak to and encourage you?

    _____

    _____

    _____

    _____

3. When you think of your current "foundation" (the memories of your history), what condition is it in? Is it faulty and broken in places?

_____

_____

_____

_____

4. In what ways can you relate to Jerry and /or Neal's stories regarding memories of their dads? (withdrawing from dad, rebelling against dad, anger at dad, hurt by dad's distance or lack of presence, empty from dad's lack of blessing or relationship)

_____

_____

_____

_____

5. "Wherever you are in your story, as you turn to the Father, know that He is _____ towards you." *p. 132*

6. Think for a moment about your story and ask the Lord to show you... "is there a blessing, a touch, a look, or a word" that is a treasure from the Father for you to discover?

_____

_____

_____

_____

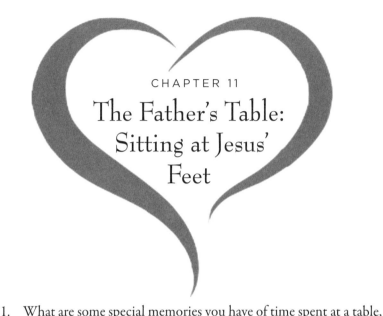

CHAPTER 11

The Father's Table: Sitting at Jesus' Feet

1. What are some special memories you have of time spent at a table, sharing a meal with others?

   _____

   _____

   _____

   _____

2. Describe a time when you "missed a moment" by being so worried/upset/stressed about doing a task.

   _____

   _____

   _____

   _____

3. Are you inclined to be more like Martha, busily preparing, or like Mary, receptively sitting at Jesus' feet?

_____

_____

_____

_____

4. "Special times of communal worship, _____

and sharing a _____ together in God's presence are

part of God's provision for our _____

and _____." *pp. 138-139*

5. Describe your daily prayer life. Are you content with it as is? In what ways do you desire change?

_____

_____

_____

_____

6. a. How has the Lord taught you patience throughout the course of your life?

_____

_____

_____

_____

b. In what ways are you waiting on the Lord, currently?

_____

_____

_____

_____

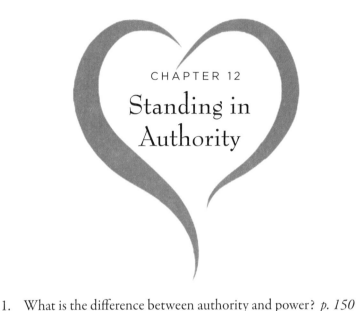

CHAPTER 12

Standing in Authority

1. What is the difference between authority and power? *p. 150*

   _____

   _____

   _____

   _____

2. What does it mean to you, to carry the Father's authority as you live out your life?

   _____

   _____

   _____

   _____

3. How do you live differently, when you're living in full awareness that you are a child of the Father?

_____

_____

_____

_____

4. What type of view on authority do you have and why?

_____

_____

_____

_____

5. a. All authority originates in _____. *p. 150*

    b. How can you grow in authority as a child of God?

    _____

    _____

    _____

    _____

    c. What are some practical ways you can exercise your faith to do this?

    _____

    _____

    _____

    _____

6. Where do you see yourself in relation to Teresa's story, between the elevator and the train?

_____

_____

_____

_____

ADDITIONAL NOTES

_____

_____

_____

_____

_____

_____

_____

CHAPTER 13

Empowered
to
Serve

1. In what ways has God used you that are very different from how you might have planned or expected?

_____

_____

_____

_____

2. "When we allow our hearts to be informed by the

_____ of the Father, we will embrace

greater _____ for the children of God,

the _____ and the _____." _p. 161_

3. What does your "field of service" look like?

_____

_____

_____

_____

4. In what two ways does humility liberate us? *p. 164*

_____

_____

_____

_____

5. Consider a situation right now in your life that needs to be transformed by God's power. How can you use the Father's authority to "bring light into darkness, love into despair, or God's power into an area of poverty"?

_____

_____

_____

_____

6. Write a simple statement of truth, that you want to recall and share, about a victory Jesus has brought to your life or about who you are as God's beloved child.

_____

_____

_____

_____

ADDITIONAL NOTES

_____

_____

_____

_____

_____

_____

_____

_____

_____

CHAPTER 14

Walking in Forgiveness

1. "_____ is the way of the Father — the way He has provided for us." *p. 171*

2. a. Are there (or have there been) people in your life whom you refuse to forgive?

   _____

   _____

   _____

   _____

   _____

b. What consequences do you experience as a result of creating this "block," by "slamming the door shut"?

_____

_____

_____

_____

_____

3. "Forgiveness is an act of the will, not a feeling." What is your response to this statement?

_____

_____

_____

_____

4. Where do we find the power to forgive? *pp. 172-173*

_____

_____

_____

_____

5. What deceptions (whispers from the enemy) keep you from forgiving?

_____

_____

_____

_____

6. Describe a time when you experienced forgiveness as a process, and forgave in stages that brought increasing breakthrough.

_____

_____

_____

_____

7. How can you know forgiveness is complete? *p. 176*

_____

_____

_____

_____

8. In what ways have you longed for "someone else's blessing" and closed your heart to what God has reserved for you?

_____

_____

_____

_____

9. a. Is there any way in which you are allowing someone else's actions to determine how you live?

_____

_____

_____

_____

b. What is one way you can take responsibility in your life and begin to experience victory?

_____

_____

_____

_____

10. What will you gain when you forgive?

_____

_____

_____

_____

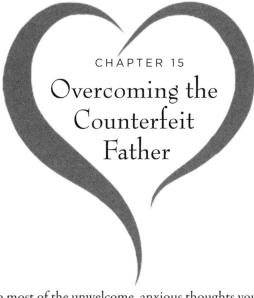

CHAPTER 15

Overcoming the Counterfeit Father

1. a. Do most of the unwelcome, anxious thoughts you struggle with seem to come from within or without?

_____

_____

_____

_____

   b. What are some of the persistent lies you struggle with?

_____

_____

_____

_____

2. "When we believe the _____ instead of the _____,
we fall under his influence . . . That being said, a believer has
_____ to fear." *p. 186*

3. Can you identify:

   a. Any roots of the lies you tend to believe?

   _____

   _____

   _____

   _____

   b. Ways in which the lies have become idols/false promises in your life?

   _____

   _____

   _____

   _____

4. Now, commit to renewing your mind. What truths from God can you identify and choose to replace those lies?

   _____

   _____

   _____

   _____

5. a. What are the three common lies people often believe? *p. 193-194*

_____

_____

_____

_____

b. Which of these particularly resonate with you?

_____

_____

_____

_____

6. What lies or spirits do you need to renounce that do not belong to Jesus or the Kingdom of God?

_____

_____

_____

_____

7. "No matter what _____ has come into your life, God's action has always been directed toward _____ and _____ you." *p. 195*

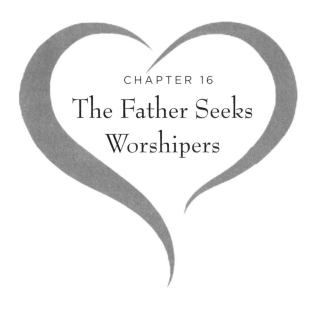

CHAPTER 16

The Father Seeks Worshipers

1. What model of worship did Jesus provide us? *p. 198*

    _____

    _____

    _____

    _____

2. "The Father is seeking _____ worshipers, worshipers who relate

    to Him without _____ or _____.

    To know Him and love Him in this way means knowing Him as

    '_____ _____'." *p. 198*

3. How does Jesus offer healing of our deepest wound, the Father wound?

    _____

    _____

    _____

    _____

4. What are some of your favorite ways to worship?

    _____

    _____

    _____

    _____

5. Describe, in practical ways, what "walking in the Spirit" means to you."

    _____

    _____

    _____

    _____

6. Throughout your time in relationship with the Lord, what has He taught you uniquely through worship?

    _____

    _____

    _____

    _____

CHAPTER 17
Conclusion

1. Note anything that the Lord revealed to you or that you experienced as you read, prayed through, and meditated on the sections in this final chapter.

_____

_____

_____

_____

2. What are the most important revelations or truths that you will take away from reading *Abba's Heart*?

_____

_____

_____

_____

3. How will you live differently as a result of what you read?

_____

_____

_____

_____

ADDITIONAL NOTES

_____

_____

_____

_____

_____

_____

_____

_____

_____

Do you want more freedom in the Father's love?

Try this "Freedom in Christ" Study Program.

The **Unbound: Freedom in Christ Study Program** has been sweeping the globe as thousands are discovering the freedom Jesus won for us. Experience the power of the Unbound Conference in your home or small group. Follow each talk with our Workbook, which includes testimonies, outlines, and daily reflections. This program includes the 8-talk DVD series and Workbook. Although not required, the book *Unbound: A Practical Guide to Deliverance* is a helpful resource.

Find these and other products at:

www.heartofthefather.com

Do you want to help others receive freedom?

Try these Ministry Training Study Programs.

Do you want to help others find freedom? The **Unbound Basic Study Program** will help you get started. This program includes the 8-talk DVD series and Workbook. Although not required, the *Unbound Ministry Guidebook* is a helpful resource. Intended for small group study, this program can also be completed alone. We highly recommend reading *Unbound: A Practical Guide to Deliverance* prior to beginning this program.

Are you looking to grow deeper in your understanding of Unbound Ministry and how to help others through Unbound Ministry? The **Unbound Advanced Study Program** will take you to the next level. This program includes a 10-talk DVD series and Workbook. Although not required, it is helpful to read the *Unbound Ministry Guidebook* before beginning this program. We recommend completing the program with a small group or with your Unbound Ministry team.

QUANTITY DISCOUNTS

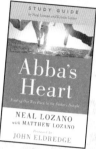

The *Abba's Heart Study Guide* is a great tool for group study. We gladly offer discounts when purchasing five copies or more of this Study Guide. For information about quantities and pricing, please e-mail: **info@heartofthefather.com** or call: **610-952-3019**

ABOUT OUR CONFERENCES

UNBOUND: Freedom in Christ conferences have offered many people a profound, life-changing experience. The conferences are the result of years of experience helping believers uncover the freedom they've been given in Christ. Join us in your own ongoing personal journey of being delivered and living the life offered to you through Jesus Christ.

For more information about leaders training, schedules, and conference registration go to:

www.heartofthefather.com
or e-mail: **info@heartofthefather.com**
or call: **610-952-3019**

UPDATES

Sign up for our free e-mail updates which include schedules and testimonies. Simply click on the home page tab: **Resources ==> eNews** found at our website:

www.heartofthefather.com

ADDITIONAL RESOURCES

To purchase additional resources, please go to our website and simply click "**SHOP ONLINE**" on our home page.

ABOUT THE AUTHORS

Neal Lozano serves as the Executive Director of Heart of the Father Ministries and the Unbound ministry efforts. Neal has more that forty years of pastoral experience helping people find freedom in Jesus Christ. He is the author of the best-selling book, *Unbound: A Practical Guide to Deliverance.* He is an international speaker and has spoken at various global conferences. Neal holds a master's degree in religious education from Villanova University, where he has also led an evangelistic outreach to students.

In addition to her role in the creation of this Study Guide, **Kristin Luther** has been an instrumental part of Heart of the Father Ministries for many years. She currently assists with a variety of administrative services, including the processing of web and phone orders, resource production, and international and bulk shipping. She lives outside of Philadelphia with her husband and four children.